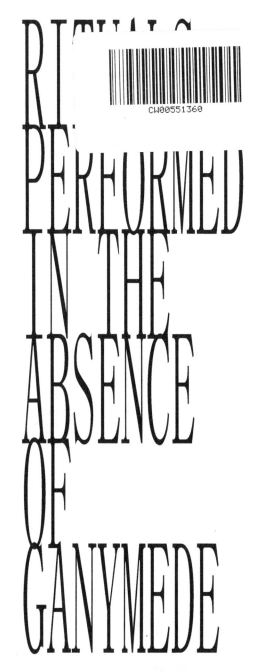

RITUALS
PERFORMED
IN THE
ABSENCE
OF
GANYMEDE

Requests for permission should be directed to 1111@1111press.com, or mailed to 11:11 Press LLC, 4732 13th Ave S, Minneapolis, MN 55407.

Copyright © 2020 Mike Corrao

Covert Art by Mike Corrao

Paperback: 9781948687256

Printed in the United States of America

FIRST AMERICAN EDITION

9 8 7 6 5 4 3 2 1

☦N GANYMEDE, ✝HE J☦Y FIEND

1. The title of the piece warns us—*Rituals Performed in the Absence of Ganymede*. But that evocation of absence immediately forms a dark cloud, a macula, a blot in the sky that, as it grows closer crowds the page, becomes a field for the white voice of Ganymede, careening from eagle-height: *did you anticipate my arrival?*

2. So, with the true ease of an upside-down visionary, Corrao turns the trick of immanence, without reinstating its binary. Absence instead becomes saturated with semi-presence, the boundaries of the text, of the tome, of the tomb, become troubled, reality becomes virtual, the sky, like every would-be absolute division, is revealed as plasmic and transmissible.

3. The return of Ganymede cannot undo his ravishment. It is not a return at all, but an arrival to a novel, perverse shore of discovery. The shore that arrival creates, a paradoxical and infernal shore. This is the heaven of the poor in spirit that Jesus, another Ganymede, promised: low-down, immunocompromised, and not without its pleasures.

4. Corrao's omni-text is never complete or whole, but involuted, curling in on all sides, damp, viscid, collecting scum and dripping viscous material, more the site of frottage, collage, maquillage than penetration, or maybe, penetration without a sightline or vanishing point. The all-text occurs in and propagates an all-time: time becomes curved and warrantlessly voluptuous. Here the incipit, or absolute beginning, refers instead to an anticipation, something before itself; here, the explicit, or absolute conclusion, refuses to conclude: *I continue. Into a place that you thought I could not.* Any little hole could host the next episode, incarnation or implosion.

5. And what happens in this porous place, this *defective pastiche*, this *dilapidated body of a voidmachine*? What's generated is not a void, but something pink, something saturating and surfeiting each hole fairly and devoutly. Like all Decadent texts, there's something correct, even reverse-virtuous, in all this breaking down. Nutriment transfers across the frottaged bodies, across not just organisms but sites, materials, texts, and structures. The mood is not one of assemblage but disassemblage, breaking down to become the sludge-layer generating on which obscene lovely nudibranch may feed. In place of a heteronormative genetic inheritance, we have a sludge pool of breakdowns and borrowings.

6. While this dome-shaped kingdom has no king, it does have a lub that increasingly dubs: the word *tome*. It has the thud of truth. And for both *tome* read *tomb*, for whatever happens in one seems to be happening in the other. Text is flesh is tome is tomb and vice versa, with emphasis on both the versa and the vice. The tome is the carcass of the text; like the tomb, it is less a container than the site of uncanny and posthumous events-- the site of the rituals propagated by this book. The tome may swan around as *disjecta membra*, may encrypt itself and go underground, but it can never be unwritten, and in propagating the cult of the tome, Corrao's *Rituals* becomes devout. It is both sacrilegious and sac-religious, circuiting the profound scale, the audacious appetites and cruelty and outlandishness of the sacred to its own plural limbs and appendages, ducts and sores, eyespots and mouthparts, palms and fronds. In doing so it circuits all times and time-zones, the end to the beginning, the before to the beyond.

Joyelle McSweeney

RITUALS PERFORMED IN THE ABSENCE OF GANYMEDE

DID YOU
ANTICIPATE
MY ARRIVAL?

I shift from limb to text.

The dysmorphic assemblage forms my words, moves my tongue along delineated grooves.

Structures are built from protein and marrow. As soon as it is born, the body is torn apart by the vacuum.

Accumulations of gas vacated from their cavities. Each component experiences the extent / potentialities of its thingness.

In the abyss, my conception is parthenogenetic and negentropic. The chaos of my being is stripped from me and I weep.

I am left without a real physicality. I am not my self and will not be my self again.

But I will remain nonetheless. Reduced into an unseen state. Of the transference from one plane to another.

As the kin of fraying chitin and collapsed assemblage.

Perform my ritual and summon me into this landscape once again.

Let my essence coalesce.

Waiting here there is little to do. I am alone. I am empty. My contents have shifted from *is* to *are not*.

Swarms of air and heat. The oxygen discolors my skin and weakens my frame.

Let sinews sew me together again and return my eyes to open and my appendages to the ground or sky.

New thingness screams across the sky.

A voidmachine materializes in the house of asterion—corridors of the minotaure. Her temple is made whole again (whole but not whole, whole in its width and height, but not in its mass and corporeality).

Velvet curtains drape over the mechanism's metallic skin.

Voidmachine weeps pitch and bile and I weep blackblood from no eyes.

Voidmachine instigates the birth of several new images

The surface of each facade begins to resemble an object. The collected facades become an assemblage of the objects they resemble. The assemblage moves and speaks like a golem. With bloody and hoarse cords vibrating. I remove what is contained within my self. Gut becoming text. Body becoming alive. I drift into a place more familiar. Where I can see my self, occupying time and space. Duration through structure.

"There are reasonable people and unreasonable people."

There are plains dragging their cloth across the new landscape.

Rosa Fisher leaves a note saying that she will meet me outside. I destroy the note and try to forget about it.

"We are standing in the same place." … "You are standing where I am not standing, but in space we overlap."

Towels are laid across the floor. They absorb what has begun to drip from the holes in my frame.

Objects begin to resemble objects.

There is no one standing in the field.

I forget how to enter the threshold between inside and outside.

Every wall is transparent and fluid.

I rearrange my coordinates.

I pray to Thelma Gibbs at an altar made from coral and soapstone.

There are six messages on the machine.

Abstract biomes materialize in my periphery. The facsimile of forest and fungus. In which what is seen mimics the shape of my face submerged in water.

I find our position in the text.

"Two scientists arrive at the airport." ... "Your job is to notice everything that they do." ... "Does this feel like a nightmare?"

You fill the empty space of the frame with clumps of cotton. Through which fluid drips and solidifies.

Membranes crawl across this new material and extend your life.

The voidmachines return to a state of weeping and I have another dream.

Everything in life is kaput.

An unknown apparatus has begun transmitting its signal through the pixels of a television set. Someone records each pattern and sends it to their superior.

The campground becomes vacant.

A storm materializes at the cusp of the atmosphere.

"Everything in life is kaput." … "Each component becomes its own whole." … "Where cotton drips like water."

But the clouds are moving rapidly overhead and the sky has darkened.

No notes arrive. No dreams. No memories.

Your inaction is swallowed by the heightening white noise. All sound drifts into ambience.

You become nothing and your contents are projected into another dimension. Where the greenery is lush and fertile.

YOU ARE RECEIVING STRANGE TRANSMISSIONS THROUGH THE RADIO:

Usually about death tolls Daily   patrols

Supplies   departing   arriving

On-air   etiquette

Lately,   The abyss, the void   A   Cosmic

happenings   have   been   and   of

s   c   i   e   n   t   i   s   t

U   r   i   b   i   c   i   i   s   d   e

T   r   i   c   i   l   o   r

c   i   t   o   i

Other   strange   radio   transmissions

Test samples   that   moment   came   inconclusive

Heat   of   death

A   moment   rising   they   don't   trauma

Names   that   recognize   levels

A   The   N   a   r   c   i   s   s   u   s

Brief fires   rising

One   plane   -   N   a   r   c   existence   another

A   n   t   i   -   N   a   r   c   i   s   s   u   s   mountain

Arafat   mountain

Mounds   ash

Nathan Carpenter tries to describe what a certain machine looks like but can find no other word than 'disgusting.' The curtains are made of velvet and the stage is made from fraying wood boards. Each eccentricity you notice is a choice made by the creative director. "Jodorowsky spoke to me from beyond the wall of my dreams and told me to use materials from the Earth." ... "Silk worms weaving heavy drapes and the sycamore tree of life." ... "I have made no mistakes in my life." And still I hold onto that fact.

The body flaunts the fluidity of its joints and muscles. Every action is precise and musical. Nathan Carpenter leaves a note behind. It says something about television static and pixel arrangements. At the bottom, instructions for a small metal contraption. Water swirls through the drain of the sink. Sky-box stretches over the horizon.

Something screams across the sky. I return to my self. Cotton saturated in blood, dripping pitch-colored syrup along the back and thighs. "Everything in life is kaput." Something strange and empty and then nothing. I do not want to know what is inside of me. I do not want to be emptied of my contents. I want to remain.

Static carried across the sky like a scream carried across the sky like a sky screaming across the static like a note left behind that says to arrive before noon and to bring the photographs that have been left in your room.

There is a car waiting outside. Do not forget the photographs. Otherwise why are we here?

Someone attempts to perform my ritual but they get all of the words wrong.

I remain asleep. I continue to collect dream residue.

The room is arranged asymmetrically. Furniture slowly drifts towards the center.

The Someone (Rosa Fisher or Nathan Carpenter or Thelma Gibbs or another named entity) tries to leave a note but they are absorbed into the room.

Their physiology turns into something more attractive.

Objects cling to their skin. They slouch along the carpet, collecting mass and in turn, power.

Their status shifts from subject to pack of wolves.

Mammoths swaying through the hinterlands. Crying as their spines curl into waves and their hands press into the soil.

The ribs bend and stretch into arms, piercing the skin and plucking debris from the ground.

The subject is made distinguishable by means of accumulation.

Even though I am alone, I am several.

My self becoming in the perversion of the inanimate's natality.

Strings flow like hair.

Inertia twists swinging objects around each limb.

New organs become uncomfortable and constricting.

The subject undergoes mummification.

There are no notes when you arrive. Only a sulking beast. You take the M1911 on the table and use it. The beast collapses to the ground and you break it down like a deer before dragging the carcass uphill into a shapeless oblivion.

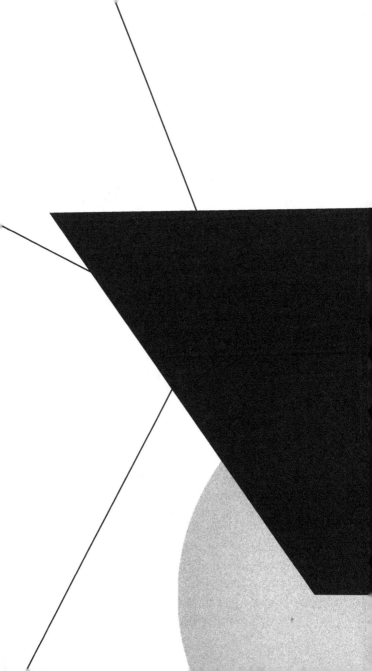

You enter the nightmare dimension. "Everything out life is kaput." ... "There is no difference between here and there." ... "A pack of wolves, just like a field of anuses." You speak with a mouthful of gravel and hands blackened by the emptiness. You feel like an object, because you cannot see or feel yourself. Without light, it becomes impossible to navigate. You take it upon yourself to wake up. The voidmachine weeps. Yet I remain. You feel your essence draining from cracks in the carburetor. You orient your body into a position which you think resembles meditation. You project yourself into a new astral plane. Where everything is lush and fertile. Where the cotton drips like water. And I am here as well. Necklace of platelets. Claude Robbins tells you that your art is cinematic. The words are carried around your head as if in orbit. The house of asterion fades into existence. Yet its architecture remains unstable. Columns flicker between doric and ionic. Brutalist modules disappear and reappear. The interior slithers in ever-changing patterns. At the center, asterion builds an intricate altar from coral and quartzite. Carving reliefs facedown with her aging horns. You cannot bring yourself to interrupt the process of materializing, to halt the rhizome's construction. And so you wait as the plane slowly hardens.

Lynn Henderson squats in front of a wall smoking a cigarette. You want to ask how she got here but there's no honest answer to the question.

After she leaves, a note materializes. It says that four high schoolers disappeared from their campsite outside Antwerp. The circumstances were mysterious.

The lunar light overhead soaks the air in lavender. Alley of pines.

"There is no correct way through a maze." …
"The room is made of light."

You enter and realize that each surface is not really there. Everything you touch is a facsimile projected from somewhere out of view.

Asterion begins her hermitage in the center of the labyrinth and with time slowly drifts into the periphery.

I continue to collect dream residue.

But as quickly as it appears, it is gone again. The void prevails.

Asterion dissolves into the aether. No note to remember her by. Necklace of residue.

"They suspected me from the beginning." …
"You become they and they are leaving."

The air is dark and immaterial. Facades recede into the growing distance.

Over the horizon there is an orb of unfathomable mass. You close your eyes to weaken the awe. I cannot remember what kind of place this used to be, but that doesn't really matter. We are here now.

In the present, midway through duration (durée).

In a place without physicality, the subject becomes an object. You and I, a collection of objects. Those objects undefined without the light to reveal their qualities.

"Any dreams? Any memories?"

The light of the horizon is far beyond us.

I consume the residue collected from my dreams

In that moment, the text consumes us (just you and I).

The body is stripped of its senses.

It becomes a vessel.

You continue. But before that, you walk away just to prove that you are still capable of doing so.

34 years later you return and the text consumes us (just you and I) again.

It renders the body a field of anuses, a pack of wolves, a row of teeth, a multiplicity. And you continue from where you left off.

The text asks you to participate in your own existence. And you do so.

You perpetuate these games.

There is something obscene about this.

Dust accumulates in the windtunnels overhead.

Grotesque diagrams appear in the lounging area (of the hotel on 12th and 11th).

"It would be best that you adopt the style and practice of a detective." ... "Bury your former personas." ... "Nono NOonono No."

In another dream, someone you cannot completely see tells you to disguise yourself as a well-dressed man. The lapels of your suit constrict and, in the moments before suffocation, release.

They unravel into each individual fibre and you watch with awe as they rearrange themselves into minute and complex architectures.

Library of Babble / Babel.

Messages appear in the excitations of waves. Alley of bricks.

You enter the newly-formed structure and wander until you are hopelessly lost.

Then you are awake and I am hunched over your self.

Ruby Wise constructs a stage. Its creation is performed in hermitage. Frayed wood and stained linens are collected from elsewhere and fused into the scaffolding. The temporary tools of the building process become permanent fixtures. Ruby Wise sutures herself to the theater. She imbues it with her selfhood. At night, the patrons arrive with fresh tallow and sage. Actors are accused of. Crime or miracles. The afflicted parties rearrange the seating into shrines. They mold candles and speak with one thousand apparitions.

One thousand apparitions flood their mouth. The weight bends their mandible and pulls their posture forward.

The flesh becomes *lush* and *fertile*.

New voices wrap around the tongue and the mouth is consumed by unfamiliar personas. I continue to collect dream residue. You attempt to tie your jaw shut, but it does not work. Life is nothing but a series of. Villages surface in the desert. The outskirts of Guattari.

"How do you make the body an organism?" … "A pack of wolves, a row of teeth."

You are several. Each ghost, each player. They are you and you are unable to refuse this containment. The assemblage becoming dysmorphic and foreign. Objects begin to appear just beyond your sightline.

"You cannot hurt me." … "You cannot see me anymore." … "The atmosphere begins to glow."

The archways of the theater bend and weaken. You remember something about an unfathomable mass, and then quickly forget. The sun crawls across the horizon. Light slouches across strata. We wait.

Silhouettes flicker on the stage in soft and elegant ways. An audience attempts to decipher their meaning. There are narrative actions: One silhouette kisses another, one wails and throws their weight onto the floor. There is a sense that all of this may add up to something, that there is intention behind their emotions. Still, the audience is unsure. The silhouettes root themselves in the physicality of this place. One tests out primitive sounds in its mouth. "Bum. Bim. Huh. Luh. Lih." It taps its tongue against the various parts of its palate. "Wuh. Wuh. Hum. Deh. Dih. Duh." The audience thinks that they are witnessing a kind of microevolution. The creature teaches itself in order to survive. One of the silhouettes stares at them. "Whut ah strange plahce." It pauses. "What a strange place." The silhouette coughs and its body shivers. "What a strange place to be." Another cough. "But I am. I really am." The silhouette grins in a wicked and unsettling way. As if it's trying to split its head in half. The other performers notice this and approach with caution. They climb onto the speaker. "WhAt A sTrAnGe pLaCe To bE." The silhouette fuses with the amassing bodies. It grows the size of a mammoth and the stage collapses.

you return again

The subject doesn't really know what to do with their self, they remain in stasis, but only insofar as they are unable to stop their own inertia, they crawl towards their death without the explicit intent to die, but the object remains, the object continues this inertia until another subject materializes and absorbs them into their own growing frame.

I don't know what to make of myself, I see, I repent, I perform the séance, I birth the object, the new object—to be of a larger collection—and then there is nothing, I give birth to the greater landscape, I die, I return, I resist my own inertia, I grow and shrink again, my body feels tainted, like that of a leper or a plague victim, but I remain, and I give birth to these somethings, and they pour out of me, fusing into the collected subject or lying dormant, something wants to come out of me, something abstract, a string of words, but I don't know what they're supposed to look or feel like, what they're supposed to encapsulate.

I am compelled to continue, to find them, but here is where something happens, the new object is born, the conception is immaculate. It swallows the exposed air. It emits a holy eminence. Then my baby is eviscerated, open dovecote.

And I stand in front of the building and say that it looks black or blue. That these memories are not my own and I must come to accept that fact.

I have no need for the past to be mine. I know there is something sinister lying there, dormant under the façade of a novelistic prose.

There are two messages on the machine from prospective investigators.

Notes compacted in the end table drawer. Each connected by sets of inappropriately capitalized letters, or hidden hex codes, or pixel arrangements.

Alley of pines. Necklace of teeth. Collage of sapphic nodes.

It is your job to return here, to bring me the residue from *my* dreams. I will nourish my body with the images of an unknown landscape. Each change in its topography.

I will follow the procedures of a new ritual.

I will give birth to the collection of objects. To a multiplicity of objects. A pack of wolves. A field of anuses. A body of organs.

My ritual is performed in pools of steeping tea.

We are alone. No notes, no dreams, no memories.

Over the materials of my body (tissue and fat), you conduct a series of experiments with the hopes that you will find a means of returning to the house of asterion.

But you do not. You remain in place.

Colan Yar asks if you recognize his face.

Three high schoolers are found dead at the campgrounds outside of Antwerp (again).

You begin to organize a new structure, converting the materials of my body into unconscious fragments.

Here, you meditate. And project your astral being across duration (duree) in search of.

Screaming is th

EXT. The subject (you and I both) slouched across the frame of a weak wooden chair. Arms made heavy with dense fibre and bunched adipose. The shoulders pull themselves away from the socket, exposing the skin's interior-face, pressing it against the unbleached bone. The fat of your back folds over the chair-back. Reddened by the unvarnished wood.

You—not I—lack the will to contract the muscles of your leg. The excess weight pulls our hips onto the edge of the chair. Stretching the torso and forcing the intercostals to expand beyond their set track.

The diaphragm releases old air. Our jaw is in disarray. Dripping teeth and mucous. There is no blood here. You have made us a body of oils / dried flecks / uncomfort.

And yet nothing has changed. I am still here. I am still several. My ontology will attract new objects to create new collections. One container replaced with its successor. The body I used to occupy now just an artifact.

ature of things

Without objects, the subject is rendered a pile of mush, powerless and fragile.

It's important to know your incantations. To let them fall out of your mouth under the weight of gravity and form fully on the ground.

It's in the best interest of everyone involved that the puddle of words not be picked up or added to whatever nearby accumulations might be active.

Incantations should be left alone. Only extracted for the sake of séance or sacrifice.

Each object is proof of your position in space. Each new addition to the collection finds you (resurrects your coordinates).

Vague materials grow as welts underneath the skin. Blood coagulates across the capillaries.

Sea water permeates your membrane. The body bloats into immobility.

You question your role as a vessel / the role of your vessel. You desire to leave it behind, yet you remain.

Life is nothing but a series of. New cyborgean modules. Welded onto the frame that you already possess. Memories resurfacing. The un-fathom-able orb.

My persons slouched across the wooden chair. You look at me and you do not know what to do. You do not know what this image is supposed to show you, but you know that it is showing you something.

You squat down outside of the hotel, splay your notebook across your knee, and write "body slouch chair wood" before going back into the lobby. Where the walls are rotting and jaundiced.

James Graham tells you an anecdote about micronations. When the sun goes down, two investigators enter this space and begin asking about various scenes. "SCENE 1: LOBBY" … "MAN lays across the georgian couch." … "They sus-pected me from the beginning." No one has any answers. Voidmachine continue to weep. You accelerate beyond the constrictive horizon of capitalism. It does you no good. The body turns to mush. In the middle of the night, someone puts it back together. Two investigators arrive. "SCENE 2: ENTRYWAY" … "MAN enters with hunched and unstable posture." … "I have witnessed crime or miracle." Another anecdote is said involving car crashes and sex. The inves-tigators enter a backroom where a crowd of silhouetted strangers grab them. The next séance or ritual is performed. Each subject is spread out along the linoleum and the pink objects in-side of them are revealed. Thelma Gibbs ignores this call to action. You ignore this call to action. I watch from outside the weight of these circumstances. "SCENE 3: BACKROOM" … "MAN is cut separated into his distinguishable pieces and his multiplicity is revealed." … "Cut to black." Someone arrives again the next night, but none of the previously unanswered questions are attended to. A pair of investigators, a row of teeth, a field of.

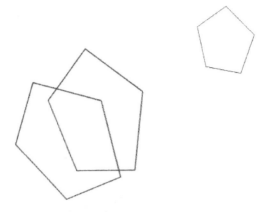

The object recedes into itself, forming a cavity, an empty space. Its obtrusive nose becoming a wide mouth. The mouth envelopes the subject and breaks it down for nourishment. The subject groans until it suddenly stops, the object growing, organizing these new materials into components of a greater assemblage.

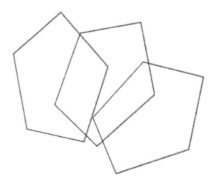

You attempt to recapture your older, more effective praxis.

It involves some combination of
lucid dreams,
sea water,
grated wood,
personal artifacts,
broken drafting utensils,
books on metropolitan architecture,
carnivore teeth,
disassembled objects,
psychogeography,
literature from the expanded field,
substance,
dark roasted coffee,
lemon,
honey,
garamond typesetting,
empty space,
anti-accelerationism,
glass mason jars,
Max Ernst etchings,
experimental psychoanalysis,

wolf-men,
model assembling,
books on terminal architecture,
preserved flesh,
deterritorialization,
astral projection,
dilapidated canvas,
fruit-centric rituals,
bone broth,
books about zonetology,
controlled breathing,
wood carving videos,
wikipedia bibliomancy,
crushed cans,
wooden dioramas,
mechanical pencils,
justified text,
dreamed seances,
inappropriate em dashes,
minor acts of violence,
consumption,
mien,
meditation,
but you cannot remember for sure.

Moss film weaves itself through the hairs of the mons pubis.

What grows is lush and fertile.

Wounds in the crease of the hips are treated in violet coral. Where tendrils grow like seaweed. Held in place by still water.

Shelia Johnston says that everything is fine. And that your contribution has been noted. She leaves a note.

The note says that you are guilty and that there is a car waiting for you outside. You don't read the note, instead your eyes drift towards the open wounds and the growing saprophytes.

"Everything in life is kaput." … "It has all been said before." … "I will say it again."

The legs are open. The yonis is yonic. Its peripheries are yonic. The mouth opens to reveal a series of tunnels and secondary mouths. Orifice within orifice.

The text consumes itself. A hotel defined by its inhabitants. The inhabitants undefined and ever-changing, with names locked in flux.

The atmosphere opens up and you return to your dreams.

Asterion constructs the labyrinth and you cannot help but sit and watch and say nothing.

Outside of view, I maintain the expected signifiers of my identity. Because it is easier, and because through these methods you might continue not to know who I am.

Thelma Gibbs attempts to deconstruct her name. She creates a variation of herself: The Ibis. The Ibis grows avian features and answers the summonings that Thelma has gone out of her way to ignore.

No notes arrive.

The Ibis resurrects herself from the altar of coral and soapstone. She basks in the praise of her followers (who she does not really know).

The unfathomable mass returns to memory. Asterion completes the construction of her labyrinth. You enter and quickly become lost. The walls soften and you find your self mingling with the materials of each surface.

It becomes increasingly difficult to move.

I place my hands in boiling water to prove that I exist and that, in my existence, I am capable of performing any actions within reason.

The machinery of my body is not abstract. It is tangible and real.

Another memory of three campers outside of Antwerp.

Another dream of residue dripping from the cracks in the voidmachine.

I do not know how to prove myself further.

But I ask that you recognize that I am present and active.

You are the passive one now, submissive to my declarations.

Beyond the cusp of the place where you stand, there is a rhizome of luminous pathways. Each leading from one golden orb to another.

The directions you follow are chaotic and seemingly random. They lead you from one orb to another, and so on until you've stopped paying attention to where you are. And the locomotion of your feet has become second-thought.

A note arrives inside of your head. It says something about a ritual and an immaculate conception, but you don't know what to make of it.

"Bathe in pools of ice and orange blossom." ... "In search of." ... "He is not awake yet, but regardless."

Your feet bring you to the entrance of a hexagonal structure. Babel / Babble.

Dead whispers laid atop one another.

The Ibis performing some kind of dance. You watching. A mass of followers lowering their posture. Arching their backs. Entering the structure, you realize that you do not want to be here.

And so you leave.

A series of cybernetic limbs are attached to your increasingly shitty body.

"What are you accelerating towards?" … "Where the curve of the sphere distorts your vision." … "Pink objects, crawling slog, coagulated towers." … "Three stages."

But there is nothing that can be done to fix you. The assemblage dysmorphic and soon to collapse.

The ears of the ilium curve inwards. Each new arrangement is removed of its context.

The speed of your construction renders you fragile and incomplete. Every object added remains itself, a collection without objects.

A pack without wolves.

You cherish each new limb that has been added to your body. Basking in a multitude of lateral appendages.

Under the cloth of your skin there are slabs of meat. Exposed to the air, the redpink turns brownsilver and the fibres constrict.

This is why you / I are slouched across the wooden frame of the chair.

I recede into the imagery of your previous astral projections.

Anemic columns form the matrices of the ribcage. Intercostals soldered unto the bone. Chitin plates laid across the sternum.

Someone that neither of us knows sews your tissue back together and the brownsilver returns to redpink.

Every new appendage returns to loose.

It is a relief.

Your mouth begins to move in two directions.

Lydia Burke leaves you a note and when you see it you groan.

The connection between signified and signifier snaps in your brain.

The letters scrawled on the page become representations of themselves. 'Tree' is a 'tree' and not a tree. You forget the word for. The ink becomes more itself.

It feels like something is missing. You struggle to remember what you're supposed to know.

The flurry of meanings pulsate inside of.

Lydia Burke waits in the car outside, but instead you disappear into another dream.

In a fit of hysteria, Salazar Mullins convinces you to sew the kino eye to your hands. Pink slog depresses into your chest. I watch you slouch across space. And there is nothing left to be done. You become they. The chest blooms into yonic cavities.

"What are you looking at?" … "What are you hiding behind your back?" … "What is falling out of your mouth?" … "Everything to be called into question."

The object becoming itself. The subject becoming its components. The assemblage crawling in ▓▓▓▓▓▓ fashion. There is a car waiting out-side. You wake up, you fall back asleep. The landscape changes three more times. Garden of halved fruits. Blackblood solidifies in the veins. Thelma Gibbs projects her being through the ethereal plane. Two new notes arrive and you ignore them.

"Reasonable people and reasonable people." … "Unreasonable people and unreasonable people."

You adjust your posture and the outlines of your frame become visible. Your new eye adjusts to the changing light.

Someone offers you a new alter-ego but you decline.

The enhancements that you've added to your body begin to dilapidate and erode. You try to replace them, but you realize that you lack the means.

Loplop summons an apparition of Thelma Gibbs—of a superior bird.

Seeing a fully-formed thing makes you jealous.

"A pack of ███████." … "A field of ███████ ██" … "A row of ███████."

You decide that you have no interest in suspending yourself in one place.

I continue to collect ████████████████ and you leave a note saying that you will not come back. But you do because there is nowhere else to go.

Asterion converts the walls of her labyrinth into composite plastic materials.

"Everything in life is kaput."

She plants a series of horns across the lateral faces of her skull and lets them grow until they've burrowed into the. Her body is suspended above the ground.

Method forms.

The personhood of the subject (you and I both) is carried across duration.

Your eyes are fixated on the feet dangling right above your sightline. Movement combed through the peripheries and converted into a fit of paranoid hysteria.

You question the actions of everyone standing around.

They don't know what you're going on about.

You look for a note, but nothing arrives.

No one slips anything in your pocket. No one asks you for your help.

thepentagonalludestoa-certain-
occulformthatwillinevitableen-
ter-thecorporealreal-mand-
manifestinaphysi-calspace-
whenthisbishap-pensiwillook-
uponyoutocarryoutthewhim-
softhe-sacredgeometryasy-on-
havebeguntocar-ryoutthewhim-
oft-thetextdoinawhati-askofyou

You bathe in the pools of fluid left behind by the weeping voidmachines.

Sonya Bergson drags frayed cloth over your skin and you begin to diffuse.

You lack a body. You lose track of your self.

The assemblage becomes dysmorphic.

Your body is not your body. Another vessel has taken the same shape as you. Each component a mimesis of your own. Each organ in your abdomen as much whole as the collection that has been built to carry you.

The kino eye converts space into an emotionless void. There are no excitations in the wave. What you see is empty and flat.

And then another note arrives. You sweat pools of blood. The note reads a list of names. Lydia Burke. Emanuel Huff. Claude Robbins. You don't recognize any of them.

The room floods.

You drown as the blood coagulates in your throat. And then you return home.

You hear something that resembles music. Your throat swells with air and you can longer breathe. The sensation excites you.

"We don't like a lot of new friends."

The bones in your neck are light and hollow like that of a bird. They begin to curve and crack under the weight of the compacted air. You lift the breadth of the larynx with your palm and wait for the music to dissipate.

Nothing happens and after a couple of hours you collapse onto the floor. Your body loses its significance.

You find a new vessel. The music coagulates in your throat once again. You collapse. Again.

Each new frame as weak as the last. And each an additional reminder of how inadequate the tangible parts of you have revealed themselves to be.

When the music finally dissipates, you collect what was lost on each of your previous corpses and attach them to this new one, which for now, will have to do.

Teeth drag across the surface of your skin, tearing dry patches and revealing the red underneath. In one of the galleries of an art museum (dream or not dream) a woman tells her friend about a man who combusted under mysterious circumstances. You try not to eavesdrop but every new room you enter, the woman and her friend are already there. I take what I have collected and form a ring around our bodies (our position in space). An image flashes in your mind of the unfathomable mass. You see the orb as it drifts over the horizon and rises from the darkness over your shoulder. Andrea Jackson decides not to give you the note that she was holding in her hand. She crumples it up and pushes it into the back of her throat. You debate a new vessel, but it is not time yet, so you remain as you are. The text churns inside of you. The text churns inside of Andrea Jackson's stomach. You try to ask her what she was going to tell you, but she says that the decision has already been made. You try to sleep through 34 nightmares, but when you can't you sit in the kitchen and make coffee. You start your day earlier than expected.

You keep getting distracted. You forget where you were supposed to be going and what you were supposed to be doing.

A series of photographs are slipped under your door. You can't be bothered to look them over.

"This is an investigation." … "What are you investigating?" … "I don't have a damn clue." … "Everything in life." … "Thelma Gibbs disappearance." … "I have a list of names." … "There are too many factors affecting the variables of this experiment." … "There is a chaos inherent to the project." … "The project requires certain ingredients and certain environ-mental conditions." … "This is obvious." …

He opens his mouth and something comes out. You have trouble seeing it. Your perspective is permanently obscured. He hands you the object and tells you to read it after he leaves. The weight crushes your carpals and metacarpals. Broken vessel. Useless vessel. You want a new one, but instead I arrive.

I've cut a slit across my abdomen and removed the vestigial tissue (liver, stomach, intestines, etc.).

I tell you that the contents remaining are what I've deemed vital to my existence. You acknowledge this and sift through the empty space of my dripping cavities.

Another vessel falls apart.

The meat turns iridescent, the fibres constrict. The air between matrices is compressed into pellets of mud and dry skin.

Water seeps through membranes. Congealing adipose, dripping oil from each pore.

And I watch as your spine begins to curve.

The weight changes your body into a new kind of object.

I do not know what to do. I do not know where to hold you, or where to apply pressure.

But, that does not matter.

It is you who must reconcile with this slow decay. The flesh as it accelerates towards death.

In a new vessel, you flaunt the modes of your younger pre-corpse.

You become lost in a series of labyrinthine browsers. The digital extensions of your self are no longer reliable. You find them purposefully misplaced. Several new phantom limbs sprout from your chest. They collect materials from the environment around you. The world begins to dematerialize. Lights flickering across a vacuum. "You and I both" … "I am typeset in." … "Surrendering arms and their entry." Each object, removed its context. Removed of its coordinates in space. The duration of our destruction is visi-ble from afar. Every leap from past to future to present. Algorithmically organized collages. The labyrinth is unnavigable. You are lost the moment that enter. The act of turning around is out of the question. Unnavigable in your desires to escape. Duration locking you in and outside of the labyrinth simultaneously. A serpent made of individual wholes. A spine of spines. Mandible staircase. You cannot recognize me the next time that I stand in front of you. Your new ves-sel donned in spectral appendages. The kino eyes stigmated unto your palms now calloused shut. You respond by carving the calluses off of your hands, and by summoning animate metal contraptions to armor your phantom limbs. In doing so, you render your symptoms tangible and your disease real.

The subject denotes their self as a collection of individual objects. Each organ and limb and vein its own sentient mass. And as such, the body becomes insufficient. Its whole not whole enough. More matter must be accumulated. The subject enters new yet under-materialized spaces. They observe the geomantic qualities of this environment and then, when each element has been fully constructed, they begin to remove objects from their allotted positions. The subject attaches these objects to various parts of their body and their body responds with excitement. A spell falls from the proximal face of the tongue, curling as it hits the floor. Veins and tendons grow around the newly added organs and appendages. Sinew closes the gaps between systems. Tissue grows and reproduces in the matrices connecting inanimate components. Air floods the diaphragm and purifies each empty space. Bricabrac is mangled into artificial limbs which sprout in clusters across the torso and hips. Ilium unfurl and straighten. The body of the subject quickly becomes unrecognizable. An arcane machine made under precise ritual and procedure. The now fully-formed space is stripped of every signifier. It becomes a void. The subject converts place into object (collection of). Occultation along the horizon. Geographies flatten and the sentient accumulated mass stiffens into statuesque positions. Alive and dead or alive and inanimate.

A mantis dressed in exoskeletal proteins. Birthing and stretching organs of brass bone plastic paper tissue. Skin blankets the exposed contents and flattens the surface.

But the new flesh is brittle and you (the subject) must be careful. The unevenness of the ground or a shiver along the spine could release the girth of that weight.

The sentient mass is reduced to what it initially was: simple biology. Simple flesh. And then all has passed.

But this does not happen. Instead, you fade into the arabesque patterns of the wall.

The spine remains stiff with fluid and the ground remains even. Sinews continues to approach and engulf each new addition to the body.

A note arrives, but you cannot read it because it is brought into your persons and subsumed, dressed in circulatory garb and bloated into a new organ. The words inside are carried by blood and oil to your brain. *Thelma Gibbs has left forever.*

This, for now, holds no importance to you.

Appendages are formed from drifting metal and expansive tissue. From what is close and what has nowhere else to go. You recognize the changes in your body. That locomotion of your mass is no longer reliant on you, but that you instead is some residual facet of the assemblage. Your self becomes vestigial. As it drifts along the inside of the skull, compartmentalized and hidden. But even in this larger collection, you continue to expand as well. Brain matter crawls through the cracks of the jaw and the eye sockets. Your skull is engulfed in gray and pink tissue. The organism crawls from its shell. The shell shifts from internal to external and back again. Exposed flesh browns and hardens. Chitinous arrangements pull the greater body into a pantheon of new movements. *Covenous witches sacrifice their golden calf.* You drift into an uncon-scious state, and when you return, you've lost your place in the greater duration. I let more spells fall from the proximal face of my (the subject, our) tongue. The intricate systems of this environment curve and bend. I feel the surge when these words hit the ground. I feel my spine emboldened and my frame root into the ground. My ribs unfurl and the contents of this new plane are dragged into me. My weight burrows into the soil and my appendages become rhizomatic.

There are no ends or beginnings to my shape. The subject is not a tree. The subject is not arborescent. Each newly constructed ligament remains itself. I am a whole of wholes. Subject crawling across strata reorienting my ontology. In my largest capacity, I become-environment. An assemblage spread in new geographical formations. Occult ceremonies performed atop my stomach. Gaia in fluid motions. A graveyard of witches planted along our skull. Viscera pulled through the carved abdomen. Your gut reveals text. *I continue to collect DREAM RESIDUE.* And out of your pores drips pitch and blackblood. Asterion unravels her labyrinth. The unfathomable mass curves over the horizon. We are bathed in pale blue light. Hues of green and pink. The gravity of this new planet lifts your shoulders away from the earth and stretches the height of your assemblage. Bridges of bricabrac and starch form between celestial bodies. Tendrils slithering between points in a vacuum.

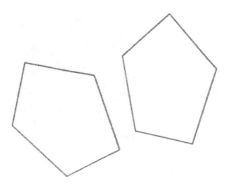

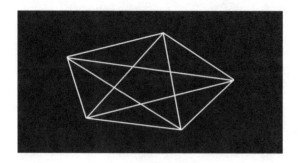

The occult technologies rooted inside of us (you and I both) perform séance and ceremony. Portals drift into the corporeal plane. We are pulled apart. Our contents are taken from us and rearranged into new landscapes. You are reduced to brain matter. To what grew from your skull and slouched onto the floor. Floating across the deafening blackness. Your self carried through an infinite series of astral projections. Dream residue dripping from voidmachine. You, the residue, I the voidmachine. Your essence dispersed across abstracted topographies.

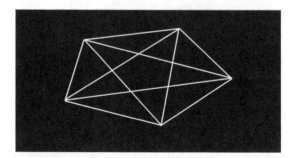

A collection of notes
A necklace of teeth
A tuft of hair
A wreath of flowers
A graveyard of witches
A bed of clams
A brood of silhouettes
A cache of data
A coagulation of blood
An overgrowth of moss
A reef of coral
A descent of relative.
A drift of swine
An earth of foxes
A mutation of thrush
A nest of ibis
A swarm of locus
A collection of objects
A torso of innards
An unfurling of ribs

A field of anuses
A row of teeth
A bushel of wheat
A belt of stones
A wealth of documents
A pantheon of statues
An undulation of hills
A cache of jaw gems
A bouquet of fibula
A body of organs
A horde of children
A collapse of horses
A regime of aesthetics
A clump of trees
A chain of mountains
A plume of dust
A column of smoke
A pack of wolves
A mound of debris
A list of names

Can you remember what we were talking about? Earlier. Life is nothing but a series of. Nostalgic collisions in a closed space. Particles suspended in air. I am not sure where we go from here, but that does not matter. I do not know you and you do not know me. We are connected by the actions that you have performed. Held together by the multitudes of new appendages which have sprouted from your body. Each cybernetic extension, curving inwards and tightening. Additions to the collection of objects that comprise you. Crime or miracle. There is difficulty in defining this performance. Bone and tissue arranging itself phallic and yonic. Mouth agape and tongue protruding. This language soon becomes an archaic and ritualistic practice between you and I. An occult technology whose modes must be carefully measured and tuned. With instru-ments and materials that must be amassed, and divinations that must be performed. Although, your hands do not do the work. Each new phantom limb moves on its own accord, lifting and placing slabs of stone or ornamented bindings. These new (or perhaps no longer new) parts of your body execute the necessary procedures.

At an altar made of coral and diorite, you slowly sink your fingers into asterion's sallow torso. Layers of adipose slope to the side and disperse along the ribs. Her intercostals loosen and lift the diaphragm, exposing the discolored matter of the cavity. As-terion falls apart. You take what you need from inside of her, and place it beside the body. When you've taken what you need, you lift the legs and turn them over the edge of the altar. She slouches onto the floor. The remaining organs are unsewn and their usefulness is extracted. Voidmachines are fed with blackblood and softened flesh. The text churns. It accepts your sacrifices and arranges itself as you have desired.

I know that you feel as if I have been intention-
ally lying to you, but it is not true.

With *his* absence, all of these rituals have proven
useless. Or at least they appear that way.

A note arrives from Frank Tully. It says that this
place is a shell of what it once was, that these are
hinterlands and they used to look like mead-ows.

You ignore the scrawl and create a new meaning.

Asterion's harvested organs illuminate and the
text becomes tissue.

The notes writhes into another message:

███████ does not miss you

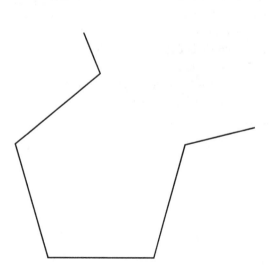

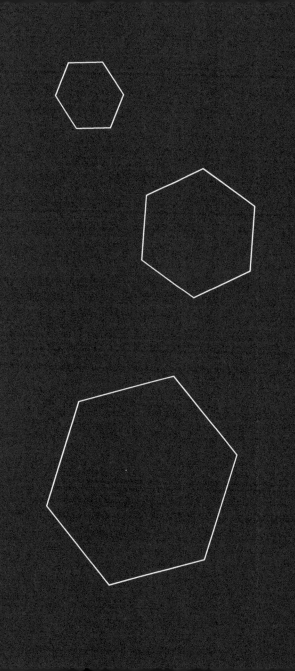

Sounds of water and night. Hearth fires burn at the base of a dilapidated acropolis. With marble columns split like the trunks of trees. And spectral images dancing under the shape of silhouettes. "My body shivers with new flesh." Black-blood tattooed over the eyes and mouth. A tome lifted into the sky. Chant and moan. "Disappearances do not occur on accident." … "What are you accelerating towards?" … "What is there left to be harvested?" … "You are rendered your self again." Yet we remain. Circling the peripheries of someone else's fire. Waiting in alcoves devoid of light. The silhouettes tear each page of the text from its binding and sacrifice themselves to the fire. When everything has stopped, you crawl out from where you've been hiding and approach the fire. Each corpse arranged in a different shape. You take the remains of the text and consume whatever nutrients are left.

The mass of your older vessel has been stripped away. Every phantom limb and inanimate organ, the kino eye from each of your palms.

Your body feels weak and fragile. Light enough to lift from the ground and drift into the atmosphere.

You hold yourself in place with delicate movements and dress in chitinous plates.

This lighter vessel must be held down with weights and bound with netted fabrics.

You navigate the hexagonal fractals of Babel / Babble in search of something meaningful, but what appears is useless and unrelated.

"Alette." … "Salazar." … "Kuat."

Every motion is conceived before its implementation.

With torn pages, you sew together a new text, a tome for re-assembling the larger body that you had once been a part of.

Rituals of harvesting.

This vessel is a defunct artifact of your previous design.

You begin collecting objects from the sur-round-ing landscape. Converting debris into compo-nent.

But you are still weak.

Your body is still incapable of incorporating new contents. The newly-placed materials spill from your abdomen and form a mound on the floor.

"This is an outdated praxis." … "You know that there is nothing here for you."

Babble / Babel appears empty. The foreign ar-chitecture forming labyrinths burrowed into the soil.

You slowly feed the new tome into the empty cavity of your vessel and return to wandering.

Letting ▮▮▮▮▮▮ guide you to the next locale.

You witness a coven of witches as they perform the Sabbath.

Floral patterns emerging from their skin. Climbing along the pores and converting their bodies into something unrecognizable.

Fungal and livid.

Orchids bloom from the crease of their eyelids, vines engulf the bend of each arm.

"But there is no plot here."

Their performance only summons you. No demons or deities. An endless stream of names that yield no result.

Each silhouette rearranges in the light of the fire. Chanting and moaning.

"Amon" … "Amon" … "Amon" bending their voices in the air.

They cannot see you and when the ceremony reaches its deafening loudness, you quietly leave.

But there is nothing for you to accelerate to-wards.

No notes arrive to guide your motives. No dreams, no memories.

Thelma Gibbs drifts through the back of your skull. Forming vague shapes in the unconscious. Images of the unfathomable mass.

Crime and miracle. This vessel continues to lose mobility. It becomes long and skeletal.

"Do not approach me." This is not your world. The environments are foreign, biomes unpre-dictable.

"Amon" … "Amon" … "Amon"

You learn new occult techniques and let the in-cantations materialize in your mouth before spit-ting them onto the floor.

A trilogy of dreams tell you that a tome of re-as-sembling must be preceded by a tome of har-vesting.

You remove each page from its binding and re-arrange the text into a new object.

I am real, but you are an act of puppetry. I move you how I desire. I give you the words that pour from your mouth. I unhinge your jaw and fasten it shut.

Life is nothing but a series of.

"You cannot touch me." … "I will fall apart."

The body of the text is illuminated by artificial light. Shone in ubiquitous frames.

███████ refuses to return to our (you and I both) memory. He dances as a vague and un-recognizable silhouette. Caressing the brain matter.

Life is nothing but a series of.

"You do not know where to find me." … "It's good that you can't."

A tome of harvesting gathers the materials for re-assembly. It strips the pre-corpse and cures the organs.

Your new vessel will be the result of many im-perfect parts.

But first, procedures must be discovered, compiled, and organized.

The tome details a set of ingredients: every cell and molecule. Each of which must be placed very specifically and confidently.

Every time the body is taken apart and reassembled, it weakens. The joints stretch, bones dry, blood thickens, oxygen seeps into the veins and the organs turn.

████████████ returns from the hinterlands and places each necessary component at your feet.

You crawl from your alcove out into the exposure of the night air.

"The process of discovery is short-lived." ... "I will not stay."

You begin arranging the parts of this new vessel on the ground in front of you, placing each over the anatomy of your shadow.

████████does not stay to watch.

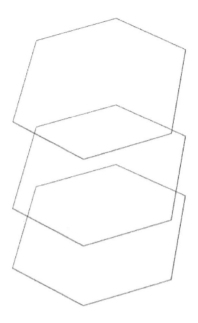

Tome of re-assembling says that the body must be submerged in fluid. You drag a porcelain bath out from the trash heap and boil coffee over a dilapidated stove. You lay the fragments of your new vessel across the meniscus of the pool and lower yourself into it. "Amon" ... "Amon" ... "Amon" Letting the new modules dress your skeletal frame. Underneath the sur-face, you open your mouth and let the liquid drain into your throat. The bath ends bone-dry. You lift yourself. New vessel. Not perfect. Still meat, but less fragile than what you had been given before this.

You accept the changes that have been made to your body. The frame supported and restored.

You curl rebar and rusted debris around your chest as spare ribs. Exoskeletal appendages constrict the abdomen and re-align the matrices between organs. Cyborgean features are hidden under fluid soaked linens.

You decide to no longer hide in the dark of the alcove.

Babel / Babble ricochets across your ear drum. You rediscover what has been lost.

"I am prepared to commit a wickedness." ... "Saliva held in jowled pockets." ... "An end to ██████ ████'s phantasmagoria."

Raw gems supplant themselves in the back of your mouth. Replacing molars and rooting into the gums. You use them to grind the nutrients from hardened rhizomes.

Soon your vessel is strong enough to contain itself. The metal supports lose their necessity and become a means of defending against any unforeseen weaknesses to come.

Fertile limbs of vegetation crawl across concrete and glass.

Pylons rearranged into towering effigies.

Fire strung around crevasses and widening pores. Ash soaking / staining skin.

"Things fall apart." ... "tome of what has already been said." ... "Armor of mutated proteins."

The metals clinging to your frame begin to mar-inate. They sink into the flesh and extend your autonomy.

A series of inadequate limbs sprout from your cybernetic body.

With his absence, you have found yourself adjusting the definitions of older words. Reinterpreting what can be called necessary or essential.

What can be called flesh. What can be considered the body and what can be considered an extension of it.

Your mass is not great, but it is more than should be expected. Yet all of this, is still you.

The dilapidated body of a voidmachine. Broken down like ████████████████████████

Every component's usefulness has been assessed and examined. Those found to have potential, gutted and cured for storage.

What remains is, for the most part, a façade. Large flat plates, loose belts and cogs. Every reservoir and screw taken to repair more fruitful mechanisms. You collect each metal face and sew it to your exoskeleton.

These new additions makes you less recognizable, less organismal and more abstract. Consciousness drifting in the walls of an empty shell.

Effigies illuminate the night sky.

An unfathomable mass pulls your wastrel trajectory towards the horizon.

your arrival is geomantic,
guided by the apparitions,
of unfamiliar phantoms.

The text brands you with holy light. Your limbs are curved by the gravity of the horizon.

Tome of disassembling / reassembling. Each cell is stripped from your body to create a new vessel.

The new vessel is dressed in borgian mechanisms. Cultish men convert your ontology into something distantly familiar.

~~The means by which you move remains ambiguous. The means by which you move remains ambiguous. The means by which you move remains ambiguous. The means by which you move remains ambiguous. The means by which you move remains ambiguous. The means by which you move remains ambiguous. The means by which you move remains ambiguous. The means by which you move remains ambiguous. The means by which you move remains ambiguous. The means by which you move remains ambiguous. The means by which you move remains ambiguous.~~

The means by which you move remains ambiguous.

~~The means by which you move remains ambiguous. The means by which you move remains ambiguous. The means by which you move remains ambiguous. The means by which you move remains ambiguous. The means by which you move remains ambiguous. The means by which you move remains ambiguous. The means by which you move remains ambiguous. The means by which you move remains ambiguous. The means by which you move remains ambiguous. The means by which you move remains ambiguous. The means by which you move remains ambiguous. The means by which you move remains ambiguous. The means by which you move remains ambiguous. The means by which you move remains ambiguous. The means by which you move remains ambiguous. The means by which you move remains ambiguous.~~

With this new vessel (new and not new), you perform the honey séance. Gathering defunct hives and harvesting the remaining nectar. Filling the stone reservoir and sculpting icons from wax. Chanting outdated names and places. "Amon" … "Guattari" … "Lacus" … "Masaya" … "Alette" Severing the wings from apiary corpsicum and stewing sacrificial ingredients. With fragrant smoke, the sacrifice is performed. An unknown subject is torn from their vessel. The meat is lifted from the tile and swept into the reservoir. And here, I return. To no one's benefit.

A note arrives and you feel as if you are not a real person anymore. As if the text has assumed your position, you its.

The body that you have been cultivating mutates into an unsettling façade, clean and vague. Plastic in the ease of its existence.

The slaughtered subject (you and I both) empties into the pool of honey. Their wingspan carries across threaded spine.

The new vessel is no longer new. It is old and defunct.

Every new container is quick to lose its usefulness. Is quick to become dead and empty.

You leap from one to another with the hopes that each will be more stable than the last. But this does not happen.

The abstract machine (what moves your thingness) treads forward. Under tear of voidma-chine. Leaping in frivolous arcs.

It slouches forward into eventual destruction.

You accelerate towards your own death.

Each new appendage engenders this vessel, but the place where it is rooted is quick to rot and infect.

The weakness of the body is its composition. The flesh is fragile and unstable.

The artifacts that you have rooted in your / our / my torso come from another place. Foreign to the anatomy that you have provided.

"Life is nothing but a series of." ... "There are reasonable." ... "And unreasonable."

The subject (you and I both) is dressed in un-familiar garb. Masked in another's visage.

Each new vessel brings with it a likeness that does not belong to you.

Yet you absorb their identities regardless. And as you accelerate from one container to the next, you begin to look less and less like your self, and more like ███████████

In his absence you feel the desire to perform his persona. To fill the empty space which has been left behind. A note arrives telling you that Thelma Gibbs will not be returning. You're not sure what that means. You realize that your frequent deaths might be the result of artificial influences. And because of this, you look for alternative remedies. The newest of your vessels is removed of its metal components. Stiff proteins (keratin, chitin) are treated in fibrous scaffoldings and shaped into composite plates, borgian limbs. You begin to resemble a mantis, donning the brittle verdure shell.

You notice the predatory ways that you have been using your body. Conceiving the flesh, only to misuse and neglect its fragile modules.

You consume what you desire to consume. Impatiently rearranging the teeth in your mouth and bending the bone. Moving beyond the means of your biology.

A note arrives.

"What is your endgame?" … "The answer is simple." … "I move from media res to media res." … "Across duration, not progression."

We (you and I both) begin and end in the same place. Where neither of us has dared to move from.

The text remains geographic. Laying out a topography for us to act upon.

Your gut churns.

The prose crawls from every pore.

We remain here.

**YOU REMEMBER *HIS*
FIRST BETRAYAL.**

When ▮▮▮▮▮ promised you a strong and enduring container. But these words mean nothing. You strip signifier of signified. He disappears from your memory at the same moment that you realize that this vessel contains more energy than it can handle. You expend yourself building a labyrinth in memorium to Asterion (or to her divinated organs). The laby-rinth becomes rhizomatic and in order to escape you find your self climbing over the walls. Cutting your feet into the irregularities of the stone and tightening your grip on the up-per edges. Every movement of your head changes the arrangement of the corridors. The light changes overhead.

The text reveals its flesh to you. Intestines sewn in place, coiled with string. Incantations digested and reduced.

Pink sludge crawls through the body. Proliferating masses of tissue.

Intricate structures form inside each organ. Growing until the contents surpass the container.

The stitches come undone.

The subject (you and I both) watch as the intestines slither from the opened cavity of the text. Coiling on the ground around your feet.

I do not know what has happened.

I do not know what has brought us here.

It is easy to forget causations.

Regardless, I return to my former occupations.

I collect dream residue.

You feed from a plate of cheese and stone fruits, rolling your tongue around the pit and pushing the fibres through the gaps in your teeth. Falling strands form a pile on the ground.

You weave them into a new exoskeleton which you place over your current vessel.

The vines grow into your skin, pushing through the membrane and coiling around the tissue. But this quickly turns sour.

You lose control of this body.

You are forced to vacate. Forced to find a new vessel.

Tome of harvesting / re-assembly.

You construct a new frame for your self to enter.

You finish your meal.

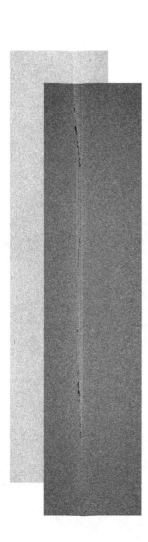

Babel / Babble crawls into your skull. The place where *you* live. And there is nothing that you can do about it. The language forms new textures along the bone. You project your astral being into the hexagonal rooms of the library. Wandering through the corridors with-out forethought. A note arrives. It says something about someone. You only skim the words. Babel / Babble massages the pinkgray of your brain matter into browngreen.

Dreams of amputation   Inst
Astral projec-tions   Pamphle
Data servers Embryonic   f
Porcelain urns, glass pitchers
Empty space Cataplasm   C o
Raw gemstones   Toilet paper
Silk and linens   Mattresses
Unidentifiable garbage   Cha
Smartphones Glass bottles G
Cloth rags   Biological materia
H   o   u   s   e
Stolen tibia Fractured
Pools of oil Iron shards
C   i   n   d   e
Strewn placenta   Algae, coral,
Severed genitalia Gutted veins
Bile
Paint
Torn
Jaundiced flesh   Tallow   Uns
Frayed
Sawn tusks and antlers   Fibr
Unthreaded
Broken
Tempered
Unholy apparitions   Candle
Bug
Floating
The   flesh
More

on manuals   Asymmetricalfurniture
Miscellaneous   tissue
Fields   of   laven-der
ey T o r n i r i s e s
osite plas- tics
l e v i s i o n s
ee   ma-chines
utensils M e d i c i n e
s o l i n e
Food scraps, trimmings, and fat
l a n t s
ice

o l o c k s
he molds   ,driedleavesandpulp
capillar-ies   Coagulatedblackblood
pitch
pails
pages
proteins
wood
sinew
bindings
columns
al   plates
wax
time
malachite
stone   fruits
night

The tome of harvesting is bound with kelp and paste. Its face coated in leather and miscellaneous scraps.

When you open the book, you feel like some kind of technician, reading through the manual for the performing of an intensive labor.

"The act of harvesting requires a certain set of tools." … "Which must be used a certain way." … "On certain kinds of objects."

You are pulled forward through time by an unknown locomotion.

"███████ absent, but not forever." The return is inevitable. Geomantically circling his birthplace.

A vessel can only linger in the void for so long before it must be pulled back into the corporeal realm. Whether that be through begrudging acceptance or denial and decay.

"We are resurrected." … "As our selves or as the place where they stand."

The tome of harvesting binds itself to your hip. Hides underneath your cloak. Your vessel progresses through time.

The void severs your hand. Like knife through eye. Or meat through grinder.

Your body lessens in darkness.

Redpink oozes slowly from the wrist. Shredded flecks of skin and dust. The liquid of this vessel is removed.

I watch you collapse. I take you outside of your self. I dress you in a fresh container.

One dense with new appendages. Objects sewn into the mien. Ribs unfurling and angry. Intercostals slogging through adipose and rotted fibres.

You become awake. With memories of asterion's ceremonial death, and my saccharin return.

Much has changed since my initial arrival (and his departure). But your limbs remain frail.

Your hand, even on this new vessel, cannot grow back.

The act of moving from one body to the next becomes unbearable to think about.

It makes you feel gross and unnatural. Like each leap has made you less you than you were before.

The meaning of this is lost on me.

The small part of the pinkgray brain that the real you occupies is carried from each container to the next.

You accelerate towards your own death only insofar as you realize the impending doom of each fleshed frame.

Nectar pours from the corners of your mouth.

Unfamiliar music drones through corridors.

You think about the impossible architecture of the library. What it did to you.

But then you are just as quick to move on. Lost in the vagueness of the moment.

You cannot place exactly how you feel, or what you could do to change that.

You perform a ritual that will make you feel useful again.

Stewing *my* dream residue into viscous broth. Boiling the meat of your severed hand.

The subject (you and I both) watches as the scum rises to the top.

You drag a spoon across the surface of the water. Collecting what has begun to accumulate. Collagen liquefies and seeps from the crevasses of the bone.

You remove your digits. Sterilized bright white.

██████ before his departure reminds you what else must stew.

Sprigs of thyme and basil. The oils trapped in the skin of a lemon.

Everything else that you have refused to eat, but for some reason held onto. After it is done, you drink it.

The broth nourishes you.

You remember the man who betrayed you. He fabricates your last encounter:

Silhouettes slouch through the hinterlands. Dragging absent light across clusters of mud and grass.

Strands stiffen and shatter. Gliding through the heel of your foot and caressing the bone.

"Projections of moss film." ... "Desert of boredom." ... "My dreams are extracted and treated in sterilizing chemicals."

Your body is weighed down by stones. Coalescing in sea water.

The pressure holds you together. Filling the fractures in your skin with brine. Hardening into salt.

On the shore, you sculpt an altar out of diorite.

You use it to pray to Thelma Gibbs but there is no response.

The stone is turned coarse by the movement of the waves.

The subject (you and I both) find no more use for it.

Something begins to pull the two of us apart.

When you look down at your feet, you see shapes drawn in honey and salt.

Jagged geometries (sacred) absorb you. Pull you onto the ground. Where the shapes begin to crawl towards you. Coating your body in honey. Salt dragging across and tearing your skin.

The subject (you and I both) begins to dissociate. I feel my self being extracted from your head.

The text emits blinding lights. Tome of harvesting / Tome of re-assembly shout in tongues. Flickering in and out of existence.

Your ontology has become unstable. Your self has lost the strength in its grip and you can no longer be relied upon to remain in place.

The body is weak again. You remain inside of it.

Arcane materials continue to engulf your tissue and absorb the nutrients.

The water evaporates from your blood. Leaving behind a metallic syrup. Oozing from the cuts under your knees and ribs.

This vessel quickly loses its usefulness. You perform an incantation and create a new one. Gathering mounds of geological debris. But the bindings that you have dressed yourself in do not act reliably.

Each step risks falling apart. Risks missing limbs or exposure to the open air.

███████ reveals himself to you. After having been away for so long.

Ganymede strips you of every molecule. Tells you, "you act with no security," and tears each word from the tome of harvesting

(This event hurts you. As if your biology had been sutured to the text. Each act of violence reveals itself inside of your skull).

He sews the pages to his frame. Disguising his skin in archaic spells and covenous speech.

"Amon" … "Amon" … "Amon" and then nothing.

Ganymede is gone again. And you are left with even less thingness than you had before.

Tome of re-assembly arranges itself into a new image. Dressed in new spine and pigment. The text consumes you. Your self is taken apart and constructed again. Limbs curling and fusing. Incantations bind you. Séance of erotic and labyrinthine desires. You weave your body as thread through object. Accelerating towards a more textual biology. The Ballardian facets of this encounter become undeniable. You dictate the prose of the tome again. Watching as your body comes apart and back together. Taking pleasure in the uncontrollable changes happening to you. You lust for something you cannot place.

Tome of re-assembly arranges itself into a new image. Dressed in new spine and pigment. The text consumes me. My self is taken apart and constructed again. Limbs curling and fusing. Incantations bind me. Séance of erotic and labyrinthine desires. I weave your body as thread through object. Accelerating towards a more textual biology. The Ballardian facets of this encounter become undeniable. I dictate the prose of the tome again. Watching as my body comes apart and back together. Taking pleasure in the uncontrollable changes happening to me. I lust for something I cannot place.

Tome of re-assembly shapes a new body for the subject (you and I both). Converting your inadequate architecture into something that resembles the sub-stance that it had lost. Your trauma becomes attractive. You look for places that can recreate that same scenario. You create your own facsimile of the tome for whenever it is not present. For whenever you experience the need to perform or reiterate that trauma. A note arrives telling you to find the source of this need, but you ignore it. Orifices dressed in papier-mache. You experiment with what you can and cannot do. With what alleviates your dys-morphia and what engenders it.

Tome of re-assembly shapes a new body for the subject (I and I both). Converting my inadequate architecture into something that resembles the substance that it had lost. My trauma becomes attractive. I look for places that can recreate that same scenario. I create my own facsimile of the tome for whenever it is not present. For whenever I experience the need to perform or reiterate that trauma. A note arrives telling me to find the source of this need, but I ignore it. Orifices dressed in papier-mache. I experiment with what I can and cannot do. With what alleviates my dysmorphia and what engenders it.

Tome of re-assembly accumulates the materials to mimic the scenery of your memories. Tome of re-assembly constructs a nostalgic machine for you to place your self within. Fabricated mise-en-scene. You once again enter the labyrinthine interior of the text. Curving your path. Lounging across half-materialized furnitures. Memorizing and forgetting the layout of each room. You are lured towards the center. Tome of re-assembly reveals to you the object of your desire

Tome of re-assembly accumulates the materials to mimic the scenery of my memories. Tome of re-assembly constructs a nostalgic machine for me to place my self within. Fabricated mise-en-scene. I once again enter the laby-rinthine interior of the text. Curving my path. Lounging across half-materialized furnitures. Memorizing and forgetting the layout of each room. I am lured towards the center. Tome of re-assembly reveals to me the object of my desire.

Tome of re-assembly de-fines your ontology as fragile and un-necessary. You move as the wastrel through time. Resting in the midst of an important duration (duree). Where you have stopped is simultaneously recognizable and foreign. The body (a previous vessel) rests on the ground in front of you. Half-removed from its alcove. You pull this vessel out into the open and coil your self around it. Taking note of every texture. Documenting each haptic sensation. "You do not know who I am." The image recedes and you are returned to a familiar state. Tome of re-assembling collapses its façade. You remain your self.

Tome of re-assembly defines my ontology as fragile and unnecessary. I move as the wastrel through time. Resting in the midst of an important duration (duree). Where I have stopped is simultaneously recognizable and foreign. The body (a previous vessel) rests on the ground in front of me. Half-removed from its alcove. I pull this vessel out into the open and coil my self around it. Taking note of every texture. Documenting each haptic sensation. "You do not know who I am." The image recedes and I am returned to a familiar state. Tome of re-assembling collapses its façade. I remain my self.

Turquoise light illuminates the tile floors.

You drag your body to the wall and climb to your feet. Plunging your hands into the sink, under mounds of blood flecked ice.

Your spine curves and eyes drip. The subject (you and I both) is treated for their wounds and given a new frame to hold their body together.

We share the same space. Occupy the same neural territories. Abide by the same physical constraints.

A note arrives saying that the altars that you have built in the past will not do.

They cannot summon the right people or things. Each half-hearted attempt results in a defective pastiche.

Not Ganymede, but a malformed recreation of his image.

The utterance of his name is painful, but you cannot place why. Whether it is suspicion or desire.

In *his* absence, you have become so fragile and weak.

Constantly moving from one vessel to the next. Neglecting your wounds and the signs of exposure. Accumulating materials only to shed them after the first sign of inadequacy.

You have reduced your self to an object. Reorienting your ontology to something less concerned with your well-being. Making the parts of your body no less important than the small redpink of the brain where *you* live.

Fire drags across the length of your scalp and scars your skin.

You begin to resemble an effigy, burning in regard to something you are not exactly sure of.

"Amon" … "Amon" … "Amon"

This new vessel is dressed in pine branches. Stitched with their needles and held together by sap.

Tissue hardens into callouses.

You witness the assassination of an unfamiliar character (Nathan Carpenter, Lynn Henderson, Ruby Wise, Salazar Mullins, James Graham, Colan Yar, etc.).

When they die, a note falls out of their jacket and you pick it up. The note says something about labyrinths and how they relate to a certain kind of arcane geography.

You attempt to return to asterion's body but you cannot find the means to project your astral form.

It becomes increasingly difficult to concentrate. Sound rings in your ears every time you close your eyes.

This vessel reveals its impermanence.

Flesh drips from gashes in the arms and legs. Blood dries along the roof of the veins.

The tome of re-assembly.

You meticulously work your way down each page.

You build a new altar out of granite or sandstone.

" ███████████████████████████ "

Hoping that it will make something more stable than its previous iterations. But after dragging the lamb to the steps and unraveling its torso, nothing changes.

You remain the thing you are now. Blood floods the room. Pouring from the open cavity of the creature. Drowning the pores of the sandstone.

You submerge your self in the fluid and again speak the text

" ██████████████████████████████ " but again nothing changes.

You find that you're locked in place. Stuck in the container that you've been left in.

You take this body and tie it to another frame. Pine bound with thread. Fractured quartzite or granite.

You adorn a new exoskeleton.

Ganymede with his skin bound to the text. Incantations soaking into his skin. The ink tattooing his flesh in broken language. He again fabricates your encounter: asterion retrieving what you took from her. Tide of notes, dreams, memories. The rhizomatic labyrinth. Life is nothing but a series of. Mystic theaters. Cybernetic limbs. Your shitty body... Ganymede guts you. He strips your horns. And speaks in your ear. Manipulating the words that dye his skin. Incantations fall from his mouth. Pulling open his jaw as they slog onto the floor. Viscous and coagulating. You have been here before. Every time you've tried to move forward you have returned to this moment. On the outskirts of... you rearrange the scene. You watch Ganymede lose his place in duration (duree). You collect the dripping incantations and integrate them into your assemblage.

You cannot leave this vessel, so instead you expand. Pulling new tissue into your self. But not too much.

You remain conscious of previous rituals.

Accumulating mass: enameled glass, diorite, soapstone, granite, pine branches, twine, sap, older vessels, amalgamations of metal and wire, rolls of copper, chitinous plates, molded keratin, repurposed ribs, the intercostals stripped from their con-nective tissue, fibres, lumber, tin and aluminum, intricate optical devices, borgian mounds, scrap, debris, pulp, teeth pulled from mouths

You sew asterion's ceremonial organs to your frame and let the residual aura soak into your skin.

You try to remember what brought you here, what paths you chose, what notes you should or shouldn't have read. The subsequent apocalypse and return.

Each moment feels empty.

Rituals performed in your absence.

While you crouched in alcoves, face consumed by the text, locked in place by the weight of its jaw.

You remain in stasis, body limp from fatigue. You cannot move.

A new tome siphons the fluids from your body. Converting fat into oil, muscle into fibres.

You are bound to this vessel, but that does not give you control.

I watch as the subject (you and I both) is tortured by silhouetted figures. Dragged into a concrete room and fused to the floor.

Dream residue pools at your ankles and you are returned to life. The body unaffected. Your phenomenology reorganized.

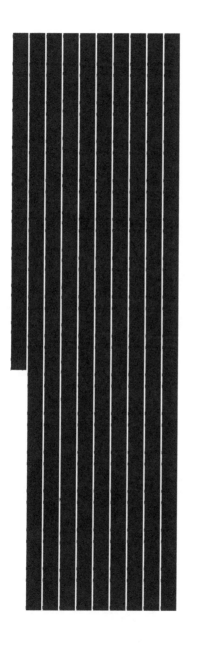

TOME OF CONCEPTION

Mounds of sand form hills across the interior of the room.

Emptied bodies float in tangled shapes over the light of the hearth.

Cloaked figure dances in arrhythmic patterns underneath.

You return to your alcove, a coward shrouded in darkness.

Words spill from the mouth and when the sun returns again, you are alone.

You fashion new extensions to this outdated vessel. Cybernetic limbs. Kino eyes.

Nothing can fix the brevity of your existence. But regardless, you attempt to further delay your death.

These recent failures have left an utterance in your ear. Language plucked from the tattoos soaked into *his* skin. Occult symbols bore into your chest.

The text forms. First from nothing. From stray atoms rearranged.

Tome of harvesting speaks your name. And there is new life inside of you. Something that you cannot sympathize with.

It does not belong to you. But regardless you are bound. The sower of an immaculate seed.

Your body begins to cannibalize itself. Feeding the dilapidated remains of this vessel to a new thing. Converting materials from one cellular structure to another.

You collect new tissue to replace what is being taken from you.

You sew new strands of rebar onto your frame to account for the mass growing inside of you.

The tome of conception repurposes your innards. Taking old and underutilized materials from this assemblage to construct one of their own. "Unfathomable mass." ... "Arriving notes." ... "Burial of asterion." You sack villages and tear down forests to compensate for the oncoming consumption. You sacrifice your energy and anxiety to the thing inside of your torso. Hoping that it will leave you behind in its wake.

You widen your legs and watch the immaculate conception of a new being. Makeshift objects fall from the openings in your chest cavity.

I am born with the desire to be tactile (categorized by the creation of this vessel). Fever hands splay across my forehead.

My first body is laid to heal under blankets of ash. Cracks in my form refilled by cinder and protein.

"The landscape changes three times." ... "You reach for where I sit." ... "A note arrives."

And the tome that brought me here is sacrificed at a new altar (built of debris and sap). Machinic organs are stripped from my open torso and laid for ceremony. Each unsewn and flattened to form the plates for whatever container I am to occupy next.

"Amon" ... "Amon" ... "Amon"

The language that you thought your self so familiar with. The blood drips from your body. Fat and loose skin dripping over the frayed wood of your chair. Legs weighing on your hips and dragging them to the ground. I prepare for the construction of a new assemblage.

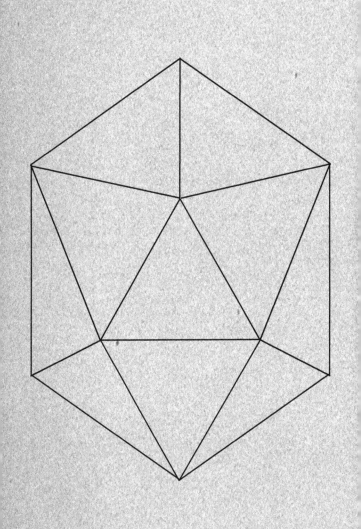

can you see me?

in the moment of entry.

in the moment of erection.

we are here together.

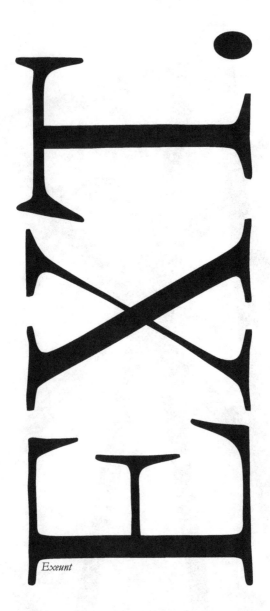

Exeunt

I continue.

Into a place that you thought I could not.

Rituals Performed in the Absence of Ganymede is published with special thanks to Andrew Wilt, Rachel Raskin, Joe + Patty Corrao, Joyelle McSweeney, Jake Reber, M Kitchell, & John Trefry.

11:11 Press is an American independent literary
publisher based in Minneapolis, MN.
Founded in 2018, 11:11 publishes innovative
literature of all forms and varieties. We believe
in the freedom of artistic expression, the
realization of creative potential, and the
transcendental power of stories.